Contents

D0551010

Caught in the Web learning activities:

Barney's Simple Safety Rules	9
Visit ThinkUknow.co.uk	11
Web Wordsearch	14
Word Jumble	17
Meanings 1	23
Online Gaming Safety Tips	24
True or False: Internet Safety	25
Secret Message	29
Help Spike Stay Safe On The Web	30
Meanings 2	31
Mobile Phone Safety Tips	35
Meanings 3	36
A Message from Barney and Echo	39
Parent Activity: Internet Safety	40 - 41
Parent Activity: Cyber Bullying	42 - 43
The UK Council for Child Internet Safety	44

Acknowledgements

The Police Community Clubs of Great Britain would like to thank the following for their contribution to this publication:

- Published by Ian Jackson
- Norman Kirtlan for creative ideas
- Paul Hogg and Mark Crombie for graphic design
- Julie Poad for learning activities
- Community Initiatives Associates for sales and distribution

The Barney and Echo series

The Barney and Echo series has been developed to support parents and teachers in addressing personal, social and health education (PSHE) at key stage 1-2. The books are set in Treetop Forest and follow the adventures of Barney Eagle and Echo Squirrel.

Each title has a story relating to a PSHE subject area with activities to reinforce the learning goals. The books, which are designed to be fun and educational, can be used in a classroom setting and at home to support reading and discussion.

The series of five books also contains titles that address issues such as anti-social behaviour, internet safety and bullying. In total, the books have been distributed to more than 350,000 children across the UK.

In this title Barney has to help his friends when they start using the internet. Barney teaches his friends the importance of internet safety, not giving out personal details to strangers, internet chat rooms and the consequences of cyber bullying.

With help from Tom Stoat the Woodland Wizard, Barney helps his friends to stay safe online.

Caught in the Web

"27...28...29...30...," Echo Squirrel was counting loudly and scribbling a list into his notebook.

"31...32...33...," Echo was so busy that he didn't see his friend Barney Eagle flutter down beside him.

"Hi Echo," said Barney, stretching out his wings.
"You look very busy. What are you doing?"
Echo smiled and held up his notebook.
"I'm making a list of all my friends and I've got 33!"
"Wow," said Barney. "That's a lot."
Echo nodded excitedly, but then the smile left his face.
"It is a lot," he said. "But it's not as many as Dizzy and Spike have."

Barney was puzzled. After all, Echo was one of the most popular animals in Treetop Forest and 33 seemed like a lot of friends.

"They've both got computers and smart phones," Echo explained. "And now they have lots and lots of new friends who they talk to on the internet. They are so busy chatting to people online that they hardly come out to play anymore."

Barney felt sorry for Echo, when suddenly the smile returned to the squirrel's face.
"But guess what Dad is getting me tomorrow?"
Barney nodded. "I think I can guess."

Echo's smile was even wider now, lighting up his whole face. "A brand new tablet," he shouted excitedly. "I just can't wait!"

Barney was pleased for Echo but also felt quite worried about his friend.
The internet can be lots of fun, he thought to himself, but it can also be quite dangerous if you don't follow a few sensible rules.

It was time to go and as Barney flew off into the sky, he made up his mind to keep an eagle eye on Echo.

The next day after school Spike, Dizzy Rabbit and Digsby Mole were all going for tea at Echo's house and to watch Echo open his new tablet.

"Take your time," said Echo's dad.
"Be careful or you will break it before you've even opened the box!" said his mum.

Just then Barney arrived.

Echo could hardly contain his excitement. His mum and dad had bought him a tablet for doing well at school and he couldn't wait to use it. No sooner had he switched it on than the screen beamed into life and a tune played.

Spike pushed forward as the friends all crowded around the screen. "Would you like me to show you how to make new friends? There's a great new social networking site called Woodland Chat, you can talk online to animals that you have never met before and make loads of new friends."

"Before you go any further we need to have some rules to make sure that you are safe when you go online," said Echo's dad.

Echo shuffled in his chair, desperate to get started.

"First things first Echo, we need to set up a password for you."
"Why do we need to do that dad?" asked Echo.
"To keep you safe. Without a password anyone could pick up your Tablet and use it," replied dad.

"But who would do that? It will only be me using the tablet," said Echo.
"People who want to pretend to be you. They could use your email, find out where you live, send messages as you and even steal from you. It's called identity theft. Will you have the Tablet with you all the time, every minute of every day?" asked dad.

"Well no, not every minute," replied Echo.

"And when you take it out, can you be sure that nobody else will ever be able to use it without you knowing?"
"I Suppose not," said Echo.

Barney's Simple Safety Rules

Be safe and have fun

Always check with your parents before going online

Remember not to give out personal information when online

Never arrange to meet someone in person that you have only sent messages to online

E-mails from people you do not know should not be opened

Your online friends are still strangers even if you have been talking to them for a long time

"Then you need a password to keep you safe," confirmed dad.
Once the password had been set up Echo's dad moved his attention to a small symbol at the bottom corner of the screen.
"Do you know what that is?" he asked.

Echo shook his head. "No idea dad."

"It's your anti-virus protection. It stops computer viruses which can infect your programmes when you are online. A computer virus can cause lots of problems and stop your computer from working. Your password and anti-virus protection are part of your cyber security. They keep your computer safe from people who might want to access it," explained Echo's dad.

Barney smiled mysteriously and began to write something down in big red letters on a piece of paper. Echo and his friends were curious to see what it was, but Barney kept it hidden until he was finished.

Finally he held up the paper.
"Think U Know," said the eagle simply.
"Think you know what?" replied Echo blankly.
Barney laughed at the confused look on his young friends' faces.
"It's a website that tells you all about how to stay safe online."

Echo couldn't wait to type in the web address: www.thinkuknow.co.uk.

The site was full of great advice on how to stay safe when on social network sites, instant messaging, gaming and how to deal with e-mails as well as loads of other great stuff.

Echo's mum and dad allowed the friends to play on his new tablet for an hour and when they eventually logged off everyone agreed how important it was to remember some simple safety rules.

Visit think U know

Remember

- When you are chatting online try not to give out any personal information about yourself.
- If you receive an e-mail from someone you don't know, NEVER open it. Tell an adult you trust.
- It's not a good idea to send a picture of yourself to someone you have only met online.
- Never give your mobile phone number to someone you have not met in the real world.
- Never arrange to meet someone in person that you've only sent messages to online.
- It's a good idea to use a nickname rather than your real name.
- It's a good idea to put your real age on your site- if you lie adults might try and contact you.

www.thinkuknow.co.uk

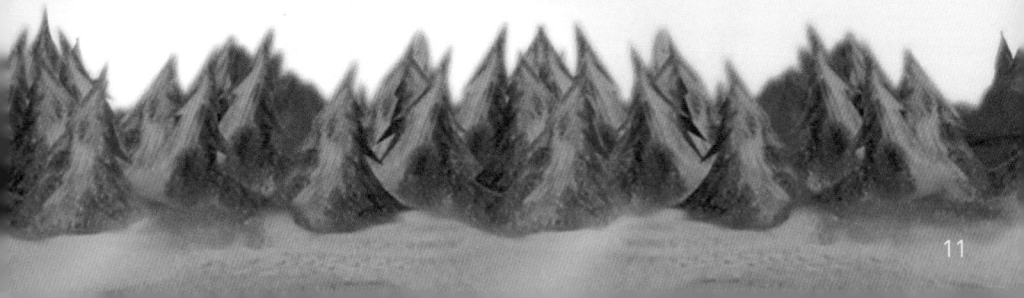

The following day, Spike was at home playing on her computer.

Her mum and dad were out at the shops and she had been told not to go online until they came home, but Spike couldn't wait. She had made a new friend on a site called HedgehogBook and Spike wanted to find out what her new friend was up to.

Spike logged on to the site and typed out a message.
"Hi Tipsy.....this is Spike....are you online?"

Spike loved social media and how it made keeping in touch with her friends so easy. She was always sending pictures to Dizzy, Echo and Digsby, showing her having fun and doing crazy things. She used her smart phone to take pictures and videos. It was simple and she could post them straight onto Headgehogbook or other sites. The apps on her phone even let her do it for free. Spike also liked Chat rooms where she could talk to people online. Sometimes it would be people she knew, but often it was complete strangers like Tipsy.

After a few moments, a message appeared from Tipsy.
"Hi Spike... yes I am online. How are you?"

The two hedgehogs chatted for a while about what they had been doing at school and a new boy band they both liked. Spike was enjoying chatting to Tipsy as they seemed to like so many of the same things.

Tipsy sent a new message.
"Would you like to meet me?"
Spike thought this was a brilliant idea.
"Yes, I would love to meet you," she typed.

"I live in Treetop Forest, where do you live?" asked Spike.
Tipsy told Spike that she lived quite close by and suggested that they meet halfway, at the castle next to the lake.
Spike agreed that Rocky Castle would be a great place to meet.
"See you on Sunday at three," she replied.

Web wordsearch

See if you can find the following words;

1) Mobile **APPS** are popular ways to play games.
2) When you are **ONLINE** in a **CHATROOM** do not give out your personal information.
3) Only open an **E-MAIL** from people you know.
4) Make sure your **GAMING** console has security settings.
5) The **INTERNET** is great fun if you are careful.
6) Your **LAPTOP** and **TABLET** should have a strong **PASSWORD**.
7) Only go on **WEBSITES** suitable for your age.
8) If you receive a nasty **TEXT** message tell a trusted adult.

W	S	K	A	L	I	A	M	E	U
E	W	P	F	G	H	Z	B	G	X
B	P	R	P	H	J	X	N	A	R
S	C	H	A	T	R	O	O	M	E
I	T	B	S	J	A	C	M	I	T
T	L	U	S	K	K	B	M	N	T
E	T	I	W	G	L	V	L	G	I
S	X	A	O	N	L	I	N	E	W
T	E	N	R	E	T	N	I	Z	T
P	T	S	D	P	O	T	P	A	L

On Saturday morning the friends were all back at Echo's house.

Echo's mum came into the room carrying a big tray.

"Who would like a drink and some ice cream?" she asked.

Everyone except Digsby Mole jumped up and sat at the table, spoons at the ready.
Digsby had been quiet all day. He shook his head.
"No thanks, Mrs Squirrel," he said politely. "I need to go home now."
Digsby left as the others all tucked in to the ice cream.

"What's wrong with Digsby?" asked Barney. "He looks very sad."
"I don't know," replied Echo.

"Digsby hasn't wanted to join in any games for a couple of days now. Perhaps it's because he hasn't got a computer or smart phone. His mum and dad can't afford one."

Barney wasn't convinced. He knew something was wrong with poor Digsby, and he was sure that it wasn't just because he didn't have a computer or smart phone.

"Digsby's worried about something," thought Barney. "And I need to find out what is troubling him so I can help."

As Barney the Eagle, together with Echo's dad watched Echo, Spike and Dizzy playing happily with the tablet, Barney hoped the three friends would remember the safety rules. But Barney worried that in all the excitement they might forget.
Then he had a great idea!

"Who wants to make the most new friends?" he asked.
Everyone jumped up and down shouting:

"Me, me, me..."

Barney laughed and said, "okay, meet me tomorrow morning at nine o'clock at Tom Stoat's house. We can have a competition. See you at nine o'clock, and don't forget to tell Digsby."
Barney said goodbye. He needed to see Tom Stoat the Woodland Wizard. He had a great plan, but only Tom Stoat could make it work.

Word jumble

Un-scramble the letters to find the correct words.

TERINTEN	.....
RYBEC GULYBLIN	.....
CHAK	.....
XETT	.....
MEALI	.....
FASE	.....
LONINE	.....
GLOBS	.....
LOPATP	.....

The next day dawned bright with only a few fluffy white clouds breaking up the sunshine bathing Treetop Forest. Tom Stoat's house was in the middle of the tall oaks, almost completely hidden from view.

Barney was perched on a branch in the tallest of all the oaks surrounding Tom's house as he watched the animals arrive.
"Is everyone here?" called Barney from above.

Echo shook his head. "I don't know where Digsby is. I did tell him to come. Perhaps he's busy."

Barney knew that something must be wrong, but decided not to say anything just yet as he watched Spike and Dizzy giggling and whispering to each other.

"Who wants to be the first to make new friends?" asked Barney.
All three leapt into the air, shouting:
"Me, me...I want to be first."
Barney held up his wing.
"One at a time," he said calmly.
"Echo, you can be first."

Echo felt a little unsure of what was going to happen as he followed Barney through the long hallway and into Tom Stoat's special room. Once inside, Echo saw a huge computer with a screen so big it filled one complete wall of the room.

"Take a seat," said Barney. "And don't look so nervous, there is nothing to worry about."

No sooner had Echo sat down than the screen lit up with a new message.

"Hi Echo. My name is Charlie Squirrel. Do you want to be my new friend?"

Echo let out a yell of delight. A new friend! His fingers reached for the keyboard and he typed a reply to Charlie's question.

"Hi Charlie. Yes please. I would love to be your friend and chat with you."

Charlie's reply came straight back.

"I live in Summertown Village. Where do you live?"

Echo told Charlie that he lived in Treetop Forest, high up in a big elm tree. He then described exactly how to get there.

"Are you at home?" asked Charlie.

Echo typed back: "No, I'm at Tom Stoat's house with my friend, Barney. My mum and dad have gone out to visit my grandmother."

Then the writing on the screen disappeared. A few seconds later up popped a picture of Echo's house.

"That's my house!" shouted Echo out loud before quietly whispering, "why is the computer showing me my house?"

Then Echo saw something else.
A squirrel climbed the tree and jumped into the house through the window of Echo's bedroom. After a few moments the squirrel climbed back out and guess what he was carrying under his arm?

That's my tablet," said Echo, tearfully. "That squirrel has stolen my new tablet. Who is he?"

The squirrel on the screen gave a big wave and a yellow-toothed smile.

"My name is Charlie!" he sneered. "Thanks for telling me everything I needed to know so that I could steal your tablet! You really are a good friend Echo."

Echo was really upset when he thought how easily he had given Charlie all of the information that he needed to break into his house.

"I only wanted to make friends," he said to Barney, still looking in disbelief at the screen.

"Don't worry," reassured Barney. "When you get back home, your tablet will still be there, but you really must think in future about what you tell people online. Especially people who you do not really know."

Meanings 1

Join the words to the matching statements using a line.
To help you, Barney has done the first one for you.

A Blog	a person who you know well and who you like a lot, but who is usually not a member of your family.
A Stranger	is someone who might 'find' their way into your computer and access your information.
A Friend	is a tool like 'Google' which helps you find information on the internet.
A Hacker	is a diary you can write online about yourself or your interests.
A Search Engine	is important to protect your computer from bugs and computer viruses.
Internet Security	is someone you should never give details about yourself to.

Online Gaming **Safety Tips**

O nly add people you know in real life, these are people you can trust
N ever be mean to someone else when you're playing a game, that makes you a bully!
L anguage is important, don't use swear words even if others do
I n App purchases can end up costing lots of money; make sure you get permission to purchase them
N obody likes to lose, but don't get too upset if someone beats you... remember it's just a game!
E njoying yourself is important, but don't spend too long playing games online

G aming can be so much fun, but make sure you tell your parents when you go online
A lways be careful when chatting to someone online - they may not be who they say they are!
M ake sure your password is strong so no-one can hack your account
I f you think you may have been tricked or cheated, don't keep it a secret. Tell someone you trust straight away
N ever give anyone your personal information
G ames are a great way to relax and have fun, but it's important to be careful about what your share online to keep yourself safe

True or False Internet Safety

	Your answer	
When you're making an account online, you should use your real name as a username	True	False
When you're making an account online, you need a strong password that no one could guess	True	False
You should tell strangers your name when you're playing with them online	True	False
When you receive an upsetting message, you should send one back	True	False
You should never agree to meet online friends, without discussing it with your parents / guardians	True	False
Not everything that you see when you're online is accurate	True	False
Send a picture of yourself to new online friends	True	False
You should make your password easy to remember in case you forget it	True	False

It was Spike's turn in the special room next. She sat down in front of the computer and saw huge words appearing one at a time.

"Hello again Spike. It's Tipsy here. Your new friend."
Spike was really pleased to hear from Tipsy. "Hi," she replied and the two friends chatted for a while about all the things that they both enjoyed, like music and movies.

"Are you still going to meet me at the castle by the lake this afternoon at three?" asked Spike.
"Of course," came the reply.

"But don't tell anyone else. Especially your parents. Let's keep this our little secret, shall we?"

Spike thought about the advice Barney had given, but it seemed like fun to have a secret meeting. Looking behind her she noticed that Barney had left the room.

"OK," she replied. "It will be our secret."

No sooner had Spike agreed and sent the message than the screen changed. The words faded away and the castle appeared. It looked huge as it filled the whole wall.

Spike wasn't sure what was happening, and then she saw herself on the screen, sitting alone in a dark cold room deep inside the castle walls.

"That's me," she said to herself. "I must be waiting for Tipsy."
But Tipsy did not show up. Spike watched as the image went into fast forward mode. In a few moments the sun slipped behind a big grey cloud and the castle was lost to a long dark shadow.

Spike felt very frightened as Barney came back into the room. "Where's Tipsy?" she asked. "Why didn't she come to meet me?"

Barney's face was very serious.

"What do you think could have happened to her?" he asked. "And what could have happened to you if you had gone to the castle by yourself?"

Spike suddenly realised how dangerous it was to agree to meet with someone she didn't know.

"And what if Tipsy isn't who she says she is?" continued Barney. "Just because someone tells you something online doesn't mean it is true. Some adults pretend to be children online. What if Tipsy was really an adult who wanted to harm you? That's why it's so important to follow the simple safety rules when you use the internet. You can still have loads of fun AND be safe."

Spike was very sad and disappointed that she had been so silly, but Barney knew she had learned some valuable lessons.

Secret Message

Fill in the missing letters to reveal the words.

1. Always tell your P _ _ _ N _ S when you go O _ L I _ E
2. When you are online never give anyone your P E _ S O _ _ L information
3. Be careful if someone asks you to keep something S _ C _ E _
4. Don't send P _ C T _ _ E S of yourself to people you don't know
5. A _ U _ TS who wish to harm you may pretend they are C _ _ L D _ _ N
6. The I _ T E _ N _ T can be great fun if you are C _ R E F _ _
7. Don't open an E _ A _ L from someone you don't know.
8. Try and make P A _ _ W O _ D S hard to guess
9. Don't talk to S _ R _ N G _ R _ online
10. Make sure you have security S _ T T _ N G _ on your G _ _ _ S console

Help Spike
stay safe on the web

Spike has a new laptop computer. Before she starts using it, Spike needs to set up a P******d and make sure A*** V***s has been added.

Spike loves to chat and she likes Chat Rooms. Spike should talk to her parents/guardians about which Chat Rooms are safe to use and what she should say in them. **Yes** ❑ **No** ❑

If you don't protect your computer with anti-virus and passwords what could happen?

Cybersecurity is very important to protect your computer. **Yes** ❑ **No** ❑
Following the rules of ThinkUKnow is very important to protect yourself online. **Yes** ❑ **No** ❑

Sometimes, Spike posts pictures of herself and her friends having fun. Is it only her friends who can see the pictures or is it possible strangers might see them as well?

It can be fun to tease friends or people you know online with texts or photos. Dizzy thought he was teasing his friend Digsby, but Digsby was hurt and upset. When that happens teasing becomes B*****g.

Meanings 2

Join the words to the matching statements using a line.
To help you, Barney has done the first one for you.

Social Media	mobile computer
Tablet	short for applications - these are shortcuts to computer programmes, often used for games and social media
Post	computer software used to prevent, detect and remove malicious software
Apps	to add content to social media
Identity Theft	create and share content and/or participate in social networking
Anti-virus Protection	where a person takes your private information and pretends to be you online

Dizzy was really curious now. He had seen his friends come out of the special room and they had both told him that it had been quite an experience. Barney had asked Spike and Echo not to spoil the surprise for Dizzy and both had kept their promise!

Dizzy couldn't wait for his turn.

Barney closed the door and asked Dizzy to sit down at the table. Once again the wall was filled with a huge picture, this time showing a mobile phone with the text message:

"Ha Ha...Digsby smells of soil...Digsby wears big glasses...Digsby hasn't got a smart phone..."

Dizzy looked shocked and turned to Barney who had a very stern look on his face.

"Do you recognise those words?" Barney asked.

Dizzy nodded. "It's what Spike and I have been texting to Digsby. It was only meant to be a bit of fun though. We didn't mean any harm."

Again, the words disappeared and a picture came onto the screen. This time it showed the forest full of police officers searching for something. They were pulling back bushes and looking in all the holes. Dizzy wondered what they were looking for.

Digsby's mum and dad came into view. Digsby's dad had his arm around his wife who was crying.

Dizzy looked across at Barney. "They are looking for Digsby aren't they?" he asked.

Dizzy began to cry.

"Please tell me Digsby is alright. We were only teasing him."
The screen went completely blank and then disappeared into the wall. Dizzy's question was not going to be answered.

"You might have thought that sending spiteful texts was fun," said Barney. "But how did they make Digsby feel? You know how upset he has been lately. What you thought of as harmless teasing has got another name: cyber bullying!"

Dizzy felt so ashamed. He and Spike were cyber bullies. They hadn't really thought about the consequences of sending the text messages. Poor Digsby didn't know who they were from and they had made him very scared and upset.

Dizzy jumped up from the chair.

"I have to tell Spike how silly we have been," he said.
"We have to find Digsby and tell him how sorry we are for being so stupid. I hope that he will still be our friend."

Barney opened the door and let Dizzy out of the special room.

"Friendship is very important," said Barney. "It doesn't matter how many friends you have, it's how you treat them and how they treat you that is important."

Mobile phone safety tips:

Keep your phone with you

If you're worried about someone taking it, keep it hidden from sight

Be careful with your number

Only give it to your friends and people that you trust

Don't lend your phone to someone you don't know

Or put it in a place where other people could get hold of it

Use a PIN

Most phones allow you to lock your phone with a PIN code. If you don't have the code you can't unlock it, so if anyone steals your phone they won't be able to use it

Don't be pressured to give your number out

If someone is pressuring you into giving them your number, tell someone about it such as a teacher or a parent

Switch your Bluetooth off

If you have Bluetooth on your phone, keep it switched off when you are not using it

Meanings 3

Join the words to the matching statements using a line.
To help you, Barney has done the first one for you.

Passwords

Chatrooms

Instant Messaging

E-Mail

Smartphone

Cyber Bullying

are places where people can chat online and send pictures

is a way of sending messages and letters over the internet

is when someone sends hurtful or nasty messages by text or online

is a mobile phone that has many of the abilities that a computer has. It may have a touchscreen, internet, and be able to run downloaded apps

help keep you safe and should only be shared with parents

lets you 'talk' to anyone on your contact list as long as that person is online. You type messages to each other into a small window that shows up on both of your screens

It was a new day in Treetop Forest as Barney glided over the sparkling river far below. From up here he could see Echo at home in the big elm tree and the rest of the gang down by the river.

Echo was sitting on a branch taking in the morning sun and getting ready to go out and play after spending an hour on his tablet. His mum and dad had agreed to let him use the tablet for a couple of hours a day, provided that he remembered how to stay safe, especially when online.

Spike was waiting to meet her new friend, Tipsy.
After being in the special room, Spike had asked her mum and dad to go with her to meet Tipsy at the castle and when Tipsy arrived, she was with her mum and dad too.
The girls were really pleased to meet each other and enjoyed chatting while the adults went for a walk around the castle.
The two hedgehogs were to become great friends.

As he dipped his wings and soared off over Treetop Forest, Barney was happy to know that all his friends were safe.

Over by the Old Mill, Spike, Tipsy and Dizzy were splashing in the shallow pools with Digsby. Spike had introduced Tipsy to her friends and they all played well together.

Barney was happy to see Digsby smiling again.
All the bullying texts had stopped and he had forgiven his two friends. It was time to buy a computer for a certain young mole who had had a bit of a sad time lately and Barney felt sure that this mole would definitely follow the rules for staying safe online.

A message from Barney & Echo

You can have lots of fun and find out interesting and useful information by going online.

But remember - follow the simple safety rules and keep safe!

Parent Activity

Remember Internet Safety

Inform your parents when you are going online
Never open e-mails from people you do not know
Tell a trusted adult if someone asks you to meet them
Everything you add to a social networking site can be copied or printed
Remember to change your password regularly
Numbers in passwords make them harder to guess
Enjoy the internet, it can be great fun
Talk to a trusted adult if you are upset or worried

Sending pictures to people you don't know is not a good idea
Ask your parents before downloading apps
Following some simple rules will help you stay safe online
Excessive use of the internet can be harmful
Telling strangers details about yourself is not a good idea
You can stay safe and still have fun online

Don't forget to bring the book back into school!

Parent Activity

Internet Safety True or False

Answer the true or false questions below, then take this book home and ask your parents or guardians to help by answering the questions too...

Circle the correct answer.	Your answer	Parents answer
1. Having a strong password is really important	True False	True False
2. If you meet someone online it is ok to give them your address and phone number	True False	True False
3. Someone you meet online has asked you to send your picture. You should say no	True False	True False
4. If you receive an e-mail asking for your password you should not reply	True False	True False
5. Passwords with a mix of letters and numbers are more secure	True False	True False
6. There is no need to have up to date anti-virus software on your computer	True False	True False
7. It is up to the internet provider to make sure you are safe online	True False	True False
8. Some people who you meet online may not be who they say they are	True False	True False
9. Setting parental controls helps keep you safer online	True False	True False

Don't forget to bring the book back into school!

Parent Activity

Remember Cyber Bullying

Cyber Bullying is when people send nasty and upsetting messages
You should always tell a trusted adult if you receive nasty messages
Bullying is never a nice thing to do to others
Every time you get a nasty message make a note of it and tell a trusted adult
Replying to nasty messages is not a good idea

Be careful who you give your mobile phone number to
Upsetting messages should always be reported
Learn the 'Think u Know' Cyber Bullying safety rules
Let a trusted adult know if you think one of your friends is being bullied
You can get lots of help if you are being bullied
It is not your fault if you are bullied
Nasty messages may seem like just a bit of fun but they are not
Good friends will always help you

Don't forget to bring the book back into school!

Parent Activity

Cyber Bullying True or False

Answer the true or false questions below, then take this book home and ask your parents or guardians to help by answering the questions too...

Circle the correct answer.	Your answer	Parents answer
1. If I am upset about being bullied I should keep this secret	True False	True False
2. All nasty messages and e-mails should be kept and shown to a trusted adult	True False	True False
3. Bullying is a normal part of growing up and should be ignored	True False	True False
4. If you receive a nasty message you should send a nasty message back	True False	True False
5. Anyone can become a victim of Cyber Bullying	True False	True False
6. You cannot spot a bully just by the way they act or post comments	True False	True False
7. Cyber Bullying affects people of any age and from any background	True False	True False
8. Many children will not speak to an adult if they are bullied as they feel ashamed	True False	True False

Don't forget to bring the book back into school!

ZIP IT

BLOCK IT

FLAG IT

Commitments to parents, children and young people

The Council is committed to working together to help keep children and young people safe online.

For children and young people, the Council will:

- Teach you about the risks online and how to stay safe: these risks are not just about what you might find, but about how you and others you meet online might behave.
- Make clear what the rules are on the websites and services that you use and what to do when you see something that shouldn't be there.
- Help you to deal with what you find online: there is always a risk of finding things that may upset you but we will help you and your parents to understand what you can do and where to go for help.
- Above all we want to help you to use the internet now and in the future, to learn, communicate and have fun.

For parents and carers, the Council will:

- Provide search options and high quality controls that you can use to stop your children seeing harmful and inappropriate content online and monitor their behaviour. This software will be easy to set up and use.

- Provide information and advice to help you talk as confidently with your children about online risks as you do about those they find offline and choose services that are suitable for them.
- Help teachers and all of those who work with your children to support them when you are not around.
- Make clear what content and behaviour is acceptable on our organisations' websites, its age appropriateness, how you can complain and what response you can expect if you are uncomfortable about what you or your children find online.
- Give your children the knowledge and skills to build up resilience to the things they find online: like the real world, we can't take away all the risks but together we can help children to learn and play safely.

For more information please visit **www.thinkuknow.co.uk**

ZIP IT

Keep your personal stuff private and think about what you say and do online.

BLOCK IT

Block people who send nasty messages and don't open unknown links and attachments.

FLAG IT

Flag up with someone you trust if anything upsets you or if someone asks to meet you offline.

UK COUNCIL FOR **CHILD INTERNET SAFETY**

The UK Council for Child Internet Safety

New technologies inspire children to be creative, communicate and learn. However, while the internet is a great resource, it is important that children and young people are protected from the risks they may encounter. The UK Council for Child Internet Safety (UKCCIS) is a group of more than 200 organisations drawn from across government, industry, law, academia and charity sectors that work in partnership to help keep children safe online.

UKCCIS achievements include the creation of:

- a family friendly internet and a code of practice drawn up by service providers following a consultation about parental internet controls;
- advice for industry providers on effective internet safety messages they should use;
- advice for industry providers on social networking, moderation, search and chat;
- and summaries of a large body of internet safety research.

Why do we need a UK Council for Child Internet Safety?

The internet is a vital part of British life, and our dependence on it will only increase as today's children and young people become adults. In 2013, 91% of all 5-15 year olds used the internet. The estimated weekly volume of internet use at home in the same year increased with the age of the child: 6 hours for 5-7 year olds, 8.1 hours for 8-11 year olds and 17.1 hours for 12-15 year olds. (source: Ofcom)

In the UK, 48% of children say there are things on the internet that bother children their own age and 13% of 9-16 year olds say that they've been bothered/upset by something online (according to EU Kids Online). Around 10% of 8-15 year olds who use the internet at home report seeing things that make them feel sad, frightened or embarrassed online (source: Ofcom).

The internet provides children and young people with a wealth of opportunities for their entertainment, communication and education. But there are also risks of harm through the deliberate behaviour of others online and through exposure to inappropriate content. As a result, if today's children are going to play their full part as digital citizens they need to be able to deal with the risks.

With regard to youth and community projects, The Police Community Clubs of Great Britain concentrate on three themes:

Education

Through the provision of books, all based on personal, social and health education (PSHE) themes and featuring our exclusive characters Barney and Echo, we intend to educate children and their carers on numerous subjects relating to the promotion of life skills, increasing self-esteem and the development of motivation in young people.

The five publications in the series are Sparky's Big Idea: Let's Talk About the Environment, The Magic Mirror: Let's Talk About Drugs, Tobacco and Alcohol, Echo's New Watch: Let's Talk About Knives, Caught in the Web: Let's Talk About Keeping Safe on the Internet and The Bad Apples: Let's Talk About Anti-Social Behaviour. The Police Community Clubs of Great Britain has distributed over 350,000 copies of these publications to primary schools and feedback from teachers and pupils alike has been excellent.

Citizenship

We will support projects seeking to develop children and young people as active citizens who can make a positive contribution to their communities. These will include activities to tackle social exclusion, truancy and bullying, working with excluded pupils and many other community-based initiatives.

Sport and Leisure

Through our established network of clubs, we will support projects that seek to provide a stable environment for children and young people and promote moral values. The potential benefit of the work carried out by our organisation is huge. It has a national network of volunteer professionals to support the development and delivery of projects and a unique means of tapping into the ideas of children and young people. The concept is innovative and at the forefront of current thinking on working with young people, promoting social inclusion and building sustainable communities.

Notes

Notes

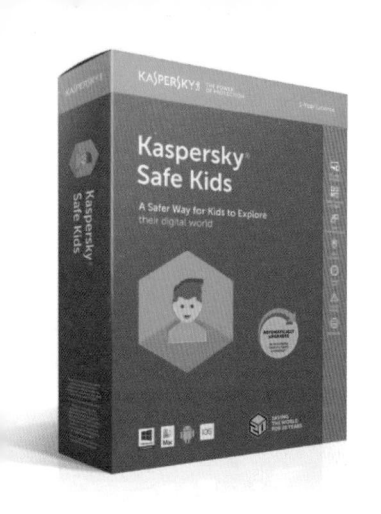

KASPERSKY® SAFE KIDS

SMARTER PARENTING – FOR YOUR CHILD'S DIGITAL WORLD

The Internet can be a powerful education tool for your children – but only if you can protect them from digital dangers.

SAFE CONTENT & APPS

It's now easy for you to guide your children away from searching for – and accessing inappropriate websites and apps to make sure, only age appropriate information is available for them to consume.

SIMPLICITY

Sometimes it's hard to know how a child's interests & emotions change over time. Activity reporting on the My Kaspersky portal in a simple way will help you understand new interests that are revealed through search topics, regular visits to websites, and apps used. It can also open up early warning signs of negative changes before they become major problems.

SAFE LOCATION

When you need to find your children, you can access a map that shows you their location – in real-time. In addition, you can see the safe area – so, if your kids move outside that area, you'll automatically get a text message or email alert.

INSTANT ALERTS

Once you set the rules for your child's digital world, instant notifications allow you to respond quickly when a child encounters restricted content, activities or other potentially unsafe situations you want them to avoid.